THE STAR FLEET

TEN CENTS
Stack no. 1 – Harbour Switcher
Captain Star's first tug.
Harbour-wise and very
experienced.

BIG MAC
Stack no. 2 – Harbour Tug
One of the biggest Star Tugs.
Strong and river-wise.

O.J.
Stack no. 3 – Paddle-wheel Harbour Tug
Oldest, wisest of the Star Tugs.
Versatile but slow-moving.

TOP HAT
Stack no. 4 – Railway Tug
Only Star Tug with a
raised wheelhouse.
Tries to avoid any
dirty work.

WARRIOR
Stack no. 5 – Harbour Tug
Very strong, but
sometimes clumsy.
Will tackle any job.

HERCULES
Stack no. 6 – Ocean-going Tug
One of the leaders of the fleet.
Very proud and rather aloof.

SUNSHINE
Stack no. 7 – Harbour Switcher
Newest member of the Star Fleet.
Works mainly with Ten Cents.

William Heinemann Ltd
Michelin House
81 Fulham Road
London SW3 6RB

LONDON MELBOURNE AUCKLAND

ISBN 434 95069 6
Based on **Bigg Freeze** , an episode of the television series TUGS,
created by Robert D Cardona and David Mitton.
Bigg Freeze was written by Roy Russell, directed by David Mitton and
produced by Robert D Cardona.
Photographs by Terry Permane. Artwork by William O'Keefe
and Stephen Lings.
Script adapted by Penny Morris. Designed by Fiona Macmillan
Printed in Great Britain by Cambus Litho, East Kilbride

Bigg City Freeze

In the 1920s tugboats played a very important part in the harbour life of all international ports. Although small, they had very powerful engines and were responsible for moving all kinds of vessels around the harbour and docks, from huge liners and cargo ships to barges and dredgers.
In Bigg City port, there were two tugboat companies operating – the Star Fleet, owned by Captain Star, and the Z Stacks, owned by Captain Zero. The two fleets were constantly competing for business, the Star Tugs by honest means. However the Z Stacks were not always so honourable...

Heinemann · London

At the time of the big freeze, when Bigg City Port was frozen up, Captain Star moved his tugs to a small port at the mouth of the river where they could carry out at least some of their normal duties.

The S.S. Vienna, a famous cruise liner, radioed for an ocean tug, such as Hercules, to help her.

As Hercules headed for the open sea, on his way to find the Vienna, he saw Lillie Lightship. She looked rather worried.

"Oh, Hercules," said Lillie. "Have you seen Ten Cents? I'm rather low on fuel, I'll need some more soon."

"I hope he's quick. If your light isn't on, I won't be able to guide the Vienna tonight."

"It's not like Ten Cents to take so long," thought Lillie.

"There's a shortage of fuel barges, Lillie. They're all frozen up in Bigg City Port. But don't worry, he'll be here soon."

Despite the cold, the tugs were all hard at work. Top Hat was grumbling as usual.

"I do so hate this awful weather. After all, I usually work at the railhead, not simply shifting barges about."

"Aye, well you'll just have to put up with it," said Big Mac. He was fed up with Top Hat's moaning.

The Z Stacks were also using the small port. Zorran appeared looking smug. He had found a fuel barge from somewhere.

"If the Star Tugs want this barge, they can't have it, right?" he said to Zip and Zug.

"You keep it, Zorran," chorused Zip and Zug. "Yes, yes, you keep it."

Zorran knew the Star Tugs were on the lookout for fuel barges. Ten Cents and Sunshine were desperately hunting for one, so that they could refuel Lillie. They knew that unless Lillie's light was working properly, the S.S. Vienna would go to another port.

"I suppose all the barges are iced up in Bigg City Port," sighed Sunshine.

Just then, Ten Cents caught sight of Zorran with his fuel barge.

"I don't believe it! Where did he get that from? Trust him. Right, come on, Sunshine," said Ten Cents firmly. "We'd better see if Zorran will let us have it."

"You'll be lucky," muttered Sunshine.

Ten Cents came up to Zorran as he approached the quayside.

"Zorran, we need a barge to refuel Lillie Lightship."

"You're not suggesting I let you have mine, are you?" snapped Zorran.

"Yes, we are, Zorran, if you wouldn't mind. You know how important it is that Lillie has enough fuel," said Ten Cents, trying to be patient.

"I know your game, Ten Cents," said Zorran. "You'll take this barge and use it to refuel the Vienna. Oh no, that's my job."

"No, it's for Lillie, honest, Zorran," broke in Sunshine.

"Wrong, Sunshine. It's for the Vienna. Delivered by me, Zorran. Got it?"

Zorran turned round and gave instructions for fuel to be put on the barge.

Ten Cents was too angry to say any more. He turned away and saw O.J. nearby. Perhaps he'd have one of his good ideas and help them.

"What is it, lads?" said O.J. when he saw Ten Cents and Sunshine coming towards him.

"O.J., we need a fuel barge," started Ten Cents.

"And Zorran's got the only one around," broke in Sunshine.

"But he won't part with it – says he needs it to supply the Vienna."

"Doesn't he realise that the Vienna won't even come if Lillie's light goes out?" asked O.J.

"Well you know what Zorran's like, O.J.," said Sunshine, feeling very cross. "He just accused us of wanting to use the barge to fuel the Vienna ourselves."

Suddenly Sunshine's expression changed.

"Hey, I've just remembered – there's a light barge kept a little way upriver from here. It's always kept filled for emergencies. It's not very far away; we could fetch that and use it."

"Brilliant, Sunshine. Let's get going," said Ten Cents. They said goodbye to O.J. and set off.

But Ten Cents and Sunshine didn't realise they had been overheard.

"What did they say, Zip?" asked Zug.

"Something about fuel and getting to the Vienna before Zorran," replied Zip, not admitting he hadn't heard properly.

"Well, we can't let that happen, can we?" said Zug.

They followed on behind the two Star Tugs.

Meanwhile, the other tugs were getting ready to take supplies out to the Vienna. Big Mac was sorting out all the new stores the cruise liner would need, and, as usual, Warrior was going to be in charge of making sure the rubbish was collected and disposed of.

He went to the rubbish quay to see if he could find an empty rubbish barge.

But because of the ice, even finding a rubbish barge wasn't as easy as usual. Warrior's normal barge, Lord Stinker, was completely full.

Warrior looked around until his eyes rested on one near him.
"That one's half-full, I mean half-empty. That will have to do."
He hitched up the barge and off he went.

As he was lumbering along, he met Zip and Zug, following Ten Cents and Sunshine.

"That's right, Warrior," they teased. "You sort out the rubbish – you should be able to do that without making a mess of it!"

"Be quiet, you two," growled Warrior. He knew he was rather clumsy and didn't like being reminded of it, especially by Z Stacks.

After a while, Ten Cents and Sunshine reached the forgotten creek where the light barge was kept.

"What did I tell you? There she is. One emergency light barge," said Sunshine, rather pleased with himself.

"You certainly know the river, Sunshine. I would never have found this creek."

"Oh, well," said Sunshine modestly, "I worked upriver for a long time so I should do."

"Right then, you take her in tow. I'll push from behind," said Ten Cents, getting into position. "We should make it back to Lillie before dark."

But Zip and Zug had other ideas. They had picked up a fire barge along the way and were now jamming it across the narrow creek blocking in Ten Cents and Sunshine.

"Oi, oi, what's going on?" shouted Ten Cents.

"Get out of that, Star Tugs," said Zip and Zug chuckling. "That'll teach you to take Zorran's work away from him."

"Well, that's really stupid. If we can't refuel the Vienna, it's as bad for you as it is for us."

But the Z Stacks were already too far away to hear.

"Oh well, we'll just have to sit here and wait for the night tide. Then when the river rises, we can nip down that gully and get back to the river that way," said Sunshine.

"But by that time, the Vienna will have already gone," moaned Ten Cents.

"No, she won't. We'll just have to be patient," said Sunshine.

Meanwhile, Hercules was approaching the Vienna.

With a whistle and a cheery "Hello, my lovely," he greeted the stately cruise liner.

She tooted in reply and signalled that she hoped all would be 'on station' for her arrival at the lightship.

"No problems, my dear. You know us Star Tugs – always reliable!" said Hercules cheerfully, not knowing that Ten Cents and the emergency light barge were trapped upriver.

Zorran was still trying to get fuel for the Vienna loaded on to his barge. The cold was slowing everything up, and he was in a very bad mood by now.

Zip and Zug appearing with enormous grins on their faces didn't make him feel any better.

"I told you to go to the lightship and wait for the Vienna."

"We thought you'd like to know that we..."

"I'm not interested. Go! I've got to wait for this barge."

Darkness was falling, and still Lillie had not been refuelled. Although her light was shining faintly, she couldn't flash it as she usually did.

Warrior, Top Hat and the other tugs were there, anxiously waiting for Ten Cents and Sunshine to arrive.

"Wherever are they? They should have got back ages ago!" Everyone was relying on Ten Cents and Sunshine. If they didn't turn up, the tugs wouldn't be able to supply the Vienna and she would go to the next port. Everyone would lose work and Captain Star would be very disappointed.

Out at sea, Hercules was on the lookout for Lillie's light.

"Come on, m'dear, where's your beam?" he muttered, trying not to let the Vienna know he was worried.

"It's almost dark. What can we do for a light?" asked Lillie.

"Anyone got any bright ideas?" asked Top Hat. "I feel a little short on inspiration I must say, chaps."

"Then we'll have to settle for any stupid ideas," said O.J. "Anyone got any of those? This is an emergency."

"Well, I could always... no, that would be stupid," said Warrior, hesitating.

"Come on, what is it?" asked Top Hat.

"Well, we could set fire to my rubbish," said Warrior.

"Well that really is a stupid idea!" Top Hat guffawed.

"It was only a suggestion," said Warrior, hurt.

"I think it's a wonderful idea," said Lillie.

As the others watched, Warrior towed his barge away from everyone else. He revved up his engine so that sparks from his stack ignited the rubbish. Soon there was a strong light.

"Bravo! Well done!" yelled the others.

By this time, Sunshine and Ten Cents had arrived. But as long as Warrior's rubbish burned brightly there was no need for the light barge.

Now finally, Hercules could see a marker light to aim for. He had begun to suspect that Lillie's light was not on, and, even though he thought the light wasn't quite like Lillie's normal beam, he tooted encouragingly at the Vienna and decided to head straight for it.

"We'll soon be at the lightship, safe and sound," said Hercules.

But the rubbish was burning fast and towing in a liner like the Vienna took a long time; soon the glare began to fade as the flames died away.

"They're letting it go out. Keep it going, m'dear, we still need it."

"It's going out. We'll have to get the light barge going now," said Sunshine. But something was wrong and it wouldn't light.

"What's the problem, Sunshine? Ooops," said Warrior, accidentally giving the light barge a hefty thump.

But as he did so, the light came on.

"Thank you, Warrior, you've been a real hero today!" said Lillie.

Warrior looked very embarrassed, but he was pleased he'd been able to help for a change.

Hercules was glad to see another light come on.

"Now that looks more like Lillie, if I'm not mistaken," he said, as they got closer and closer.

Just then, Zorran arrived with fuel for the Vienna.

"Those Star Tugs not got you any fuel, Lillie? Disgraceful!"

"Oh, is that for me? Thanks, Zorran," said Lillie, gratefully.

"'Fraid not, Lillie. This is for the Vienna," said Zorran.

Lillie looked very disappointed.

Zip and Zug had been very surprised to see Ten Cents and Sunshine.

"How did you get past that fire barge?" they asked.

"What's this?" asked Zorran, as he overheard what Zip and Zug were saying.

"We blocked them up a creek to save the fuel contract for you, Zorran," said Zip, proudly.

"We only wanted the light barge because Lillie was short of fuel," said Ten Cents, angrily.

Zorran looked furious.

"You idiots. We all needed that light here, didn't we? So the Vienna could be brought in – for us, as well as for them. Put the fire barge back in the right place before the Fire Chief finds out."

Zip and Zug went off. They had got it all wrong again.

"Well, that was OK – but let's hope next time Bigg City Port will be open," said Big Mac when the tug had unloaded.

Zorran pushed forward and waited for the fuel hose to be let down so the refuelling could begin.

But the Vienna had enough fuel to last her until the next port of call and Zorran was turned away.

"Oh, thank you, Zorran," said Lillie.

"Don't thank him, Lillie. It's only because he's lumbered with it," said Sunshine, who had seen what happened.

"I'll take it for half-price then, eh, Zorran?" Lillie smiled.

"Good idea, Lillie," said Ten Cents. "Then we don't tell the Fire Chief about Zip and Zug, OK?"

In a few minutes, Lillie's light was shining once again.

"You look lovely, Lillie," said Warrior, blushing. "Like a star."

"You were a bit of a star yourself this evening, Warrior," replied Lillie. "Thanks to you and your rubbish the Vienna got here safely after all."

THE Z STACKS

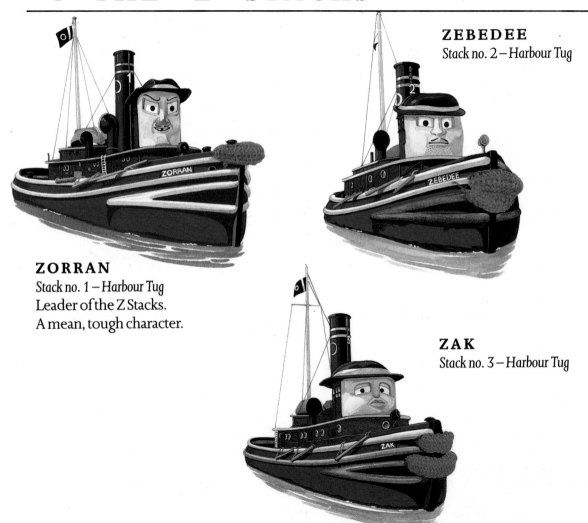

ZEBEDEE
Stack no. 2 – Harbour Tug

ZORRAN
Stack no. 1 – Harbour Tug
Leader of the Z Stacks.
A mean, tough character.

ZAK
Stack no. 3 – Harbour Tug

ZUG
Stack no. 4 – Harbour Switcher

LILLIE LIGHTSHIP

ZIP
Stack no. 5 – Harbour Switcher

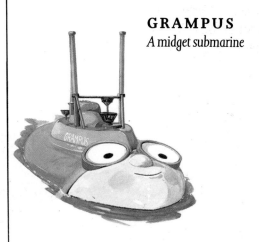

GRAMPUS
A midget submarine